patchwork QUILT PATTERN coloring book

Mary McEwen

Star of Bethlehem

Patchwork Quilt Pattern Coloring Book

ISBN 978-1-73-544951-7

Mary McEwen | Juneau, Alaska | mary.mcewen.books@gmail.com

Windblown Star / Balkan Puzzle

Ribbon Star

Storm at Sea

Log Cabin

Courthouse Steps

Diamond Star / Amethyst

Old Poinsettia / Trailing Star

Doris' Delight

Snail Trail

Eight-Pointed Star

Hexagons / Grandmother's Flower Garden

Tumbling Blocks / Baby Blocks

Brick Wall

Windblown Star / Balkan Puzzle

Night and Day / White Cross

Ribbon Star

Storm at Sea

Log Cabin

Courthouse Steps

Diamond Star / Amethyst

Optical Illusion

Old Poinsettia / Trailing Star

Doris' Delight

Snail Trail

Eight-Pointed Star

Printed in the USA
CPSIA information can be obtained
at www.ICGtesting.com
LVHW061939171223
766712LV00003B/59